TUNDRA III

EVEN MORE CARTOONS OF A NORTHERLY NATURE

By

Chad Carpenter

'97

Published by
Todd Communications
203 W. 15th Ave. Suite 102
Anchorage, Alaska 99501 USA
(907) 274-8633 Fax (907) 276-6858

TUNDRA III – Even More Cartoons of a Northerly Nature
By Chad Carpenter

Please mail US$13 in the U. S. or US$16 outside U. S. (includes postage and handling) for each additional copy of *TUNDRA III – Even More Cartoons of a Northerly nature* to:

Todd Communications
203 W. 15th Ave. Suite 102
Anchorage, Alaska 99501 USA
(907) 274-8633   FAX (907) 276-6858

Also available at the above prices: TUNDRA © 1993 and TUNDRA II © 1994, Chad Carpenter's first and second books of cartoons.

Wholesale quantities also available at reduced rates. Please call for more information.

First Printing: May 1995
ISBN 1-878100-67-X
Printed in the United States of America

Dedicated to

an absolutely smashing chap
and all around good egg. . .
my publisher, **Flip Todd**.

7

13

14

DOG OUTHOUSES

ALTHOUGH DOG FIGHTS AND COCK FIGHTS WERE A POPULAR SPORT OF THE EARLY 1900'S, **CLAM FIGHTING** NEVER SEEMED TO CATCH ON!!!

RIP HIS THROAT OUT SWIFTY!

19

25

26

SURE IS QUIET OUT HERE...
ALMOST TOO QUIET...
©Tundra 1994
Chad Carpenter

MAN-O-MAN, CHAD... YESTERDAY'S TUNDRA CARTOON SURE STUNK! WHAT WAS IT WITH THOSE TWO GUYS IN THE WOODS SURROUNDED BY MIMES...?!
©Tundra 1994
HEY! I'LL ADMIT IT WASN'T MY BEST, BUT IT SURE SEEMED FUNNY WHEN I THOUGHT OF IT...
Chad Carpenter
WELL IT SURE AS HECK LOST SOMETHING IN THE TRANSLATION, PAL! I'VE HAD GAS PAINS FUNNIER THAN THIS...!
BEEN COMPLAINING TO CHAD ABOUT HIS CARTOONS AGAIN?
HOW'D YOU GUESS?

38

40

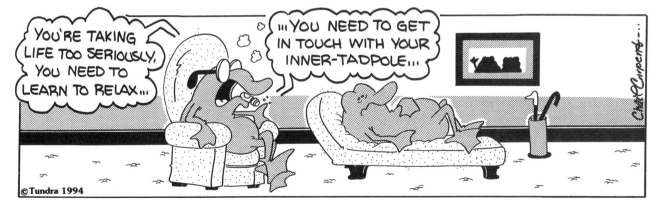

51

54

56

61

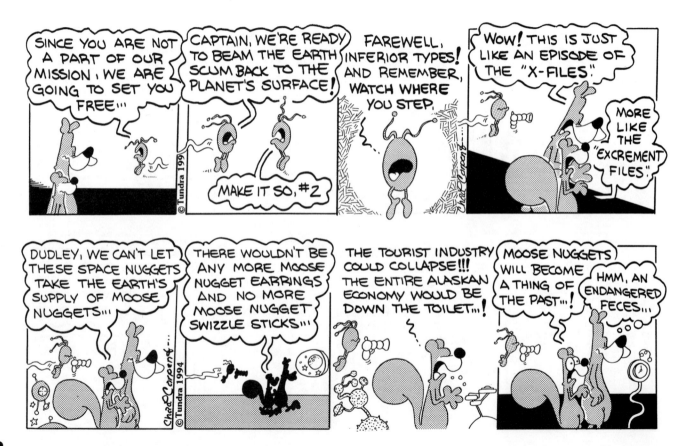

63

64

71

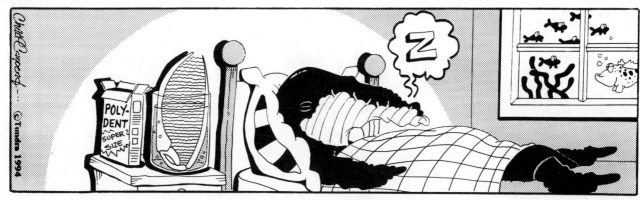

80

82

93

94

98

100

104

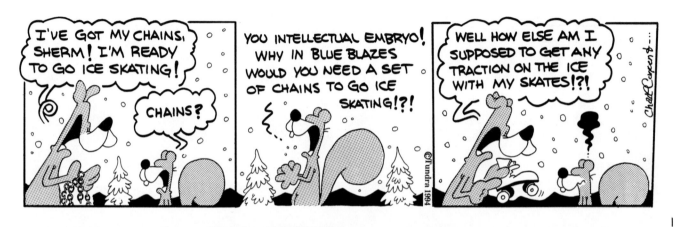

DOG MOSHING

About the Cartoonist...

Born of royal blood, Prince Chad lived a life of wealth and privilege. Chad's days were spent playing polo, fox hunting and hanging out at family reunions looking for a suitable bride. However, while the grand castles, spiffy clothes and rich foods were swell, Chad longed for something more. . . **to be a cartoonist!** So, disgracing his family, Chad abdicated his throne in pursuit of this goal. Although he shall never possess the power and respect of a king, Chad still encourages people to address him as "His Highness."

Chad, seen here with creative consultant, Rosie, keeping up with current events, so as to deliver his adoring public the best in up-to-date, cutting edge humor. . .